Cuppa Cute

A fashion inspired journal

by Ronnie Walter

A note from Ronnie:

Welcome to your coloring journal, a place where you can write down your
thoughts and dreams, while coloring all the cute illustrations and sayings!
I recommend using fine tipped markers, colored pencils, watercolor pencils
or pan watercolors. A heavy application of paint can make the paper buckle
a bit so I would use a light hand when using water based paints. If you
use markers, slip a scrap piece of paper between the pages in case of
bleed-through..

But the most important part? Don't forget to have fun!

Ronnie

www.ronniewalter.com

FABULOUS! TRENDY STYLISH UNIQUE DESIGNER

- -

- -

- -

- -

- -

- -

- -

- -

- -

- -

- -

- -

- -

- -

- -

How Tragic To Lack The Ability To Accessorize

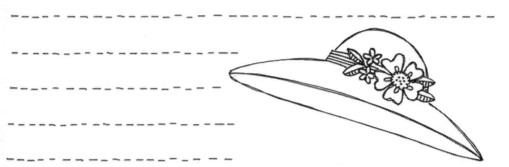

The DIVA has spoken

Made in the USA
Middletown, DE
19 May 2018